DAVEY'S PILOTS
AND THE
SEA WOLVES

IN THE BAY OF FUNDY

TALES OF THE SEA

by Catherine L. Brown

PETHERIC PRESS LIMITED - HALIFAX, NOVA SCOTIA

MCMLXXV

First Edition
JUNE 1975
ISBN 0-919380-18-2

BOOK DESIGN BY MARY ELIZA FRANKLYN

PRINTED IN CANADA
BY McCURDY PRINTING COMPANY LIMITED
HALIFAX, NOVA SCOTIA

Dedicated to the Memory of

H. L. Brown

Contents

Preface

These stories are from the diary of the late H. L. Brown, mate of many small vessels sailing in the Bay of Fundy, and compiled by his sister. There may be discrepencies in wind and sail but, please take the stories as tall tales for pastime reading.

Parrsboro, N.S. Catherine L. Brown

Fundy Tide

The Fundy Tide swirls high
To flail the rocky steep.
Fierce master with his hungry wolves
Hunts unwary ships and men.
Those who defy the surging wrath,
He wraps within a heavy shroud of fog.

Wakened by his snarling pack,
Shades, once caught in Tide's vast sweep,
Rise from shadowed mists of time.
Davey's pilots of the deep
Aid the foundering and the lost,
Guiding them through rip and shoal.

—Pamela Thomas

Sea Wolves

It has always struck me as odd that people think they have to go to foreign countries to see strange sights. We have, right here in Canada—Nova Scotia, in fact—one of the most beautiful, strange and cruellest sights in the world.

In the Bay of Fundy, in places, the tides rise to sixty feet in six hours and fall as quickly. There are terrible tidal rips and currents and all the devils' company play there.

All the old-timers, in the know, call them Sea Wolves.

Some of the best sailors in the world were born on or near the Bay. They would sail ships all over the world, only to come back to be drowned in sight of their old homes.

I used to go to the water front every chance I got—skipping school often—to sit on the cap of the wharf, talking to Captain Hube. He was old now, but had sailed small and large ships, and had been 'all over', as they say.

One Fall, he was coming home in a small packet freighter, (he owned and sailed). He struck her on a ledge in a gale NNW and at low tide. He was found the next day on the beach, the only one of a crew of three that got ashore. He was always a little odd after that trip.

The Capt and I got to be good friends; he would tell me the strangest stories about the Sea Wolves! It took me sometime to see them his way. When doubtful, he would remind me about boasting of my Irish great-grandmother and her weird tales of the 'wee fairies'.

'Watch', he'd say, 'watch'. I'd watch the currents where they were swirling by the pilings of the wharf and whisper, 'Wee fairies!, show me!' Then I'd see them! Wee wolves, sliding, swishing, curving and curling and almost I could hear them call.

One day when the tides were high and the current stronger than usual—I Saw One! A Big One! It came sliding in with the current, mean and vicious. It had a head like a wolf, no ears, small mean eyes and a big mouth with sharp teeth—long and death dealing. The front feet like flippers with long claws. The rest of the body was like a sleek fish.

That's the way Capt Hube told me they would be— half wolf, half fish. That was my first one. Since, I've seen many of them. Odd or not, I know the old Capt was right.

Often I've told the story of the Sea Wolves, when ashore, and sure was kidded!

So, I began to think that Capt Hube and I were tarred with the same brush. Sea wolves and wee fairies! Indeed!

When I went home and told old granny—she smiled that kind, toothless smile of the old, (she was past ninety) and patted my hand—'I know they were there. When your grandfather was in the Indies trade . . .' her old eyes closed, she was far away, 'but he fooled them. He died ashore.'

The Slack Coal Mystery

She was a small coasting schooner with one topmast and three headsails and was in the Bay of Fundy trade. She had been built for the lumber trade; her after cabin was on the deck. She had no quarter on her, but had a stand built around the wheel, so you could see over the house. Her galley was built forward of the cabin and was fastened to the deck by wire slings that went over it, set up with lanyards, to ring bolts in the deck.

The Captain and owner had loaded coal late in December but got 'froze in' before he could get out of the river. At the first sunning in March, he shipped a crew to go to sea.

'Well,' old Hube said, 'I was one of the crew. We didn't have to sign articles in those days in the coasting trade. She was supposed to carry five of a crew but the Skipper was a hard boiled man, so we went to sea with three, all told. Captain, mate, and a cook. I was the cook and crew member.

'There was no gas engines in those days. We got out anchor, made all sails, done the pumping by hand. So you see, between cooking, pumping, pulling on jigs, chooch tacklers and jib-sheets, I was kept pretty busy.

'We dropped down with the tide with a light, fair wind. We went to anchor, at low tide, off French Cross, on the South Shore. At high water we got underway. The wind came up S.W. and we started to beat out of the Bay. She wouldn't do over four knots on the wind and washed like a half-tide ledge.

'But, she was fairly tight. The Captain decided to stand over to the north shore, as the wind would likely draw off the land at night.

'We got over to the north shore, after a day or so, and got a bit of a slant out of the mouth of the Bay. We were somewhere between Briar Island and Gannet Rock.

'The wind had been S.W. and blowing hard all day. It was getting along towards night. The Captain said to tie up the mainsail. We would dog her under reefed foresail and stern staysail. We tried to get the old girl snugged down, but our troubles started.

'There was a hell of a sea running; she was rolling and washing bad. The old gear began to let go. Our main sheet parted after we had the mainsail down and tied up. The main boom was going from the rigging. By a fluke, the mate hooked the crock tackle in the sling band as it swung by. He nearly went overboard, but we got it back fast.

'We were pumping every chance we got; we hadn't had a suck on her for hours. Then the mate discovered the small hatch that the windlass had knocked loose and a lot of water had gone down it. She was leaking bad and also taking an awful washing.

'We had ropes made fast to the main boom with bowlines in them, which we put around ourselves, so we wouldn't get washed overboard.

'We'd been pumping five or six hours and getting pretty tired. Then came up a hard thunder and lightning storm. The lightning was as bad as I'd ever seen. The flashes would light everything as bright as day. The ship was a hard looking sight with only a reefed foresail and one headsail on her and shipping water sheer poles high.

'Everytime an extra big one boarded her, we would climb on top of the galley. Once, after an awful sharp flash of lightning, she fell off in the trough of the sea. We saw a big comber coming for us. The next minute it boarded us and took the galley right over the rail, the mate on top of it. He caught the topmast back stay, as he went by, then climbed aboard again.

'I was near drowned, but I hung onto the pin rail that was on her mast, until the sea run out of her.

'The mate took a look to where she had pulled the ring bolts out of the deck. He told me to go to the cabin and make some plugs to put in the holes. Said to hurry and he'd keep the pump going. When I got back to the wheel, the Captain wasn't there. So, I rolled the wheel up some, put the becket on it and went into the cabin.

'The Captain was sitting on a chair in the corner, holding his face in his hands. I spoke to him but he didn't answer.

‘I made more plugs in a hurry and got back to the deck. We, the mate and I plugged those holes while I told him there was something wrong with the Captain.

‘You keep pumping and I’ll see what is wrong, he said.

‘He must have been gone an hour. I was pretty tired. When the mate came back he looked exhausted.

‘The Captain just came to himself again, he said. He doesn’t know what happened to him; but, he wants us to keep pumping if we can.

‘We had been on deck for twenty-four hours. We were wet, hungry and tired. We’d pumped twelve hours and hadn’t got a suck on her. We were played out. Then I think to myself —‘to hell with her. She’s going to sink anyway. Me for the cabin and some rest.

‘When I got back to the wheel the Captain was there. He looked alright and asked if we had struck the pump. I said NO . . . and we’ll never get one. Coal loaded, as she is, she’ll sink. I’m going to lay for awhile.

‘I went into the cabin and laid down on the floor, in the corner so I wouldn’t roll around. I wasn’t a bit scared of getting drowned; I was just tired out.

‘When the Captain came in, he looked at me a minute then said—Pretty tired, are you Hube?’ ‘Yes, sir,’ I said.

'Well Hube, I'll tell you something. I've been going to sea for fifty years; I never knowed of a vessel sinking loaded with slack coal.

'Is that right, sir?

'Yes, Hube, that is true.

'Well, I think to myself, if she isn't going to sink we got to pump her out.

'I got up and went to help the mate at the pump.

'Fine, Hube, we'll soon get a suck on her,' he said.

"It was nearly noon the next day, before we got it. The wind had shifted, the sea run down a lot by then. We had something to eat and a rest. Then we made sail and made Yarmouth the next day.

'The skin was peeling off the Captain's face. He went to see a doctor and was told he had been struck by lightning.

'I have often thought IF . . . the mate hadn't caught that top mast back, when the galley was washed off . . . OR . . . if the Captain had been killed when he was struck by lightning.

'Well, there would have been another notice in the Shipping News: Lost: With all hands.

"And, I have a funny idea, to this day, that a vessel won't sink loaded with slack coal. For, you see, I believed him that night.'

Ghost Ships

After I got older, of course it was the sea for me. We sailed the coast in summer—lumber for New York, coal back. In the Fall we would load potatoes for Cuba and carry hard pine out of the Gulf ports all winter. In the spring it was a load of molasses for home consumption.

One Fall I thought I'd stay home for the winter; I'd saved a little money so thought I'd loaf; but, by Christmas, I was ready for the sea. I heard there was an American three-masted schooner in the Bay; the Captain was looking for a mate. It was his first trip in the Bay and he was having some hard luck. He was loaded two days but the tides had 'nigged' on him, and she wouldn't float until the tides got high again. Then the mate got sick and was in the hospital.

Well, he got her out and the pilot had brought her into the Bay, now he was looking for a mate that knew the Bay to go out with him. Anyone that knows the Bay of Fundy won't go out of it, in sail and heavily loaded, in the winter. There are hundreds of miles of mud flats and if there comes a snow storm and it turns cold, in a few hours you have great fields of slush ice and if you get caught in it—well, you just about have to go where it takes you. And that is generally, right over some reef or ledge and that is about the end of all hands.

Someone told him about me so he looked me up. He was a State of Mainer, a hard man and knew his business. He said he would make it 'worth my while' to go out with him—wouldn't listen when I tried to tell him it would be better to tie-up for the winter.

'No, by God! he said, 'I'll take her out or leave her bones on the beach.'

So I said, 'O.K. I'll go.' We shook hands on it then went to the hotel for a drink.

'I'll be aboard before high water,' I said, 'get the pilot to set me off. We'll have to get down to the Island on the ebb.'

He went aboard right away and I got there before high water and it's quite a job to get underway. She was a big three master and built of oak and had a high rail and was in the lumber trade. That type of schooner gets awful wet with the under-deck cargo; as so much water stays on deck when it gets a washing. She had a steam donkey in her and we used it. It was quite a change for me as I was used to hard pullers. She carried four men before the mast and a second mate that looked after the donkey engine. We should never have gone out of the Bay without a bigger crew.

The wind was up so we beat down to the Island and went to anchor at low water. We had to wait there until the wind came fair, for you can't beat out of the Bay in winter time.

There isn't any harbour, nor even a safe anchorage for many miles from where we were anchored. Nothing but that hellish run of tide.

The wind went west and blew hard for two days and it turned awfully cold. I knew there would be ice coming down on any tide now. I remember I said to the Captain one night, 'God, I wish it would snow.' He looked at me as though he thought I was crazy.

'Oh, I forgot. You don't know the Bay. Well, generally, if it snows the wind most always hauls into the north.'

'God', he said, 'I hope it snows.' Then we both laughed.

That night some field ice came down with the tide. I was pretty uneasy and was on deck every two hours. I knew we would have to get out of there very soon. The next morning it started to snow and sure enough the wind hauled into the north. We got underway an hour before high water. The Old Man wanted to put topsail and flying jib on her but I advised against it.

'We'd better wait until we get down to Quaco and see what it is like down there,' I said.

When we got clear of the Island he was damn glad we didn't have any topsail on her. It was whistling about N.N.W. and scant for our course out of the Bay. We had to take the spanker in and reef it. Before dark we'd all wished we had double reefed her all around. By then it was howling about N.W. by N. and our course was west. It was snowing so hard and she was making ice fast, that we couldn't reef more if we wanted to. I figured she didn't any more than hold her own all that flood tide. We were to the eastward of Quaco Ledges and heading right for them. We figured we were about twelve off.

We decided, after hours of ebb tide we'd keep off a couple points and go south of them. We had too much sail and she was iced so bad we couldn't drive her hard for there is a hell-ish sea on the ebb with the wind against it. I stayed on deck with the Old Man till we kept her off; we set the spanker sheet until it would lift some. She would take a rouse in a sea, knock some ice off but almost as soon as it went it would ice again as it was bitter cold.

'Better get below for a couple hours rest,' the Old Man said. Neither of us had been off deck since early morning; I knew he wouldn't leave the deck that night. 'I'll call you if I get uneasy.' He sure was some man and had confidence in me.

The cook was up so I got some hot coffee and had a smoke, Then I laid down; I didn't take my oilskins off, just slackened my rubber boots down over my heels and kept my hat in my hand. My eyes just seemed to close when someone shook me. With one pull of boots I was on my feet in a second and ready to go. Rubbing my eyes I looked at the man that wakened me. It was Captain Hube!

'What in hell are you doing here, Captain?' I asked. The schooner was riding easy and things seemed quiet. I wondered where the Old Man was and if he was alright.

'Never mind, Bill, Captain Sanford wants you to come aboard right away. He sent me with a boat for you.'

'What! on a night like this?' I was appalled.

'Never mind,' he said again. 'Come on, follow me, Bill.' It was a command. He went up forward companion-way and I followed. When we got on deck I saw there was a blinding snow squall and I couldn't see five feet ahead. There was the boat with five sailors in it and one of them was hanging onto the mizzen rigging with an old fashioned boat hook. Captain Hube jumped into the boat and I followed. He shoved her off and the men bent to the oars. She moved away easy and I noticed there was no ice on her.

It was cold and blowing as hard as ever with some vapor making. We got nicely away from our schooner, then I saw a small barge standing towards us. As we got nearer the fore lower topsail was backed and we went around the stern and went aboard at the mizzen riggin'. The barge seemed to hang on top of the sea for I stepped right aboard her as did Captain Hube.

I heard him tell the men to drop the boat astern and go for some coffee. We went aft on the lee side of the quarter deck. The officer of the watch had just got her felled away again. She only had fore and main lower topsail, two headsails and a storm trysail on her. She was just dogging back and forth across the Bay. There was no ice on her nor any water coming aboard. She seemed to be loaded light with some under deck cargo. She was old styled rigged and was in good shape and very clean—her decks scrubbed white.

Captain Hube spoke to the officer of the watch and made me acquainted with him—his name slips me—although I thought I'd seen him some place before. We went down the companionway and Captain Hube knocked on a door, said: 'Bill is here, sir.'

'Come in,' a voice called out.

I opened the door and stepped into one of the nicest cabins that I had ever been in. There was a big man at the chart table working over the chart; his back was towards me.

'Just a moment, Bill,' he said.

I had time to look around. The cabin was big, it took all the after end of the house. It was finished in either mahogany or walnut; it was beautiful and so clean. There was a swinging oil lamp in the center of the ceiling and a small adjustable lamp over the chart table.

He swung his chair around and got up. He was a mighty big man and at least six foot four. He came over to me and held out his hand: 'Glad to see you, Bill. I've heard a lot about your doings.'

'I've seen you before, sir,' I said. 'When I was a small boy. I don't suppose you would remember; you were always talking to the wharf rats.'

'I remember you, Bill. You were about eight and thin weren't you?'

'Yes,' I replied. He stood looking at me over his steel rimmed glasses that slid down over his nose, but, there was a twinkle in his eyes.

'So you're a mate now?' he asked.

'Yes, sir. I never came out of the Bay this late in the winter; in fact, I shouldn't have come at all only that damn Yankee I'm with was bound to sail. He's a stranger in these waters and sure has lots of guts to look for trouble at this time of year. So I thought I'd better come along.'

'Show me your position on the chart,' he said.

I went to the chart table saying, 'Here is the way I figger it, sir. When we were three hours past the Ile Haute we got the flood tide. The wind was N.W. by N. We were hauling west and I figgered we weren't making any headway, and also the 'seawolves' were pushing us a mile in the hour to the N.W.

against the sea and wind. I made allowance for that, so I figger we are abeam of Quaco Ledges and somewhat south of them.'

'You kept a good log on her, Bill,' he said, 'but when you were ice-bowing the tide you didn't cut to the windward as fast as you figgered. The 'sea-wolves' got scared when they saw us coming up to keep an eye on you. It was on account of them we got permission to patrol the Bay.'

He put his finger on the chart, 'There's where you are, Bill, five miles off the Ledges, south and abeam of them. In another hour you can haul up and you will be alright. By this time tomorrow night you should be abeam of Point La Pecau. Captain Abbott is patrolling off the Point and will send for you if necessary. You were with him a trip or two?'

'Yes, sir. I sure would like to see him,' I said.

'He often talks about you. He will tell you all about our job here in the Bay. Well, I'd better set you aboard now; your skipper will be getting uneasy. You better have a drink before you go.' We drank to each other.

He called Captain Hube and gave him a drink also and then Captain Sanford said, 'You'd better get Bill back aboard as quick as you can. His Skipper will be wondering where he has gone and if he finds out—well!' he drawled with a gleam in his eyes. 'Don't worry anymore for you are alright. The vapor will soon be as thick as mud, haul her up in an hour and watch her sharp.'

'Come on, Bill,' Captain Hube said, 'I'll have you aboard in fifteen minutes; we're hove-to right close but, we can't be seen in this vapor.'

I shook hands with Captain Sanford and he said, 'I'll send for you again sometime and we'll have a yarn about old times.'

'Thank you, sir. There are a lot of things I'd like to ask you.'

I followed Captain Hube on deck; it was cold out and the vapor was thick. I noticed the mate had the barge on the starboard tack close-hauled to the wind and just had steerage on her. I caught a glimpse of our schooner down to the leeward and quite close by. She was making heavy weather while the little barge was as dry as a duck's back.

'Come on, Bill,' called Captain Hube as he jumped into the barge. I hated to follow but one must finish a nasty job. The sailors pulled away, in a few minutes we were down around the stern of our schooner and along the lee side. I said good-bye to the Captain and sailors, then jumped for our mizzin. They all waved and the barge made way; I caught a sight of her going down across our stern to pick up Captain Sanford's boat.

I went down to the cabin and sat on a bunk. One of the sailors came in and said, 'The Skipper wants you on deck, Mate.'

I jumped to my feet and said, 'The vapor has set in as thick as mud.! 'It sure is bad out there,' the sailor replied.

I went on deck and found the Skipper braced against the house on the windward side. God, it was cold and the vapor cut through you like a knife.

'You'd better go down and get thawed out, sir,' I said.

'About where do you figger we are now, Bill?' he asked.

‘Have you been steering the same course, sir?’ I asked.

‘Yes,’ he answered.

‘We are about five miles south of the Ledges and they are about to point aft of the beam. We’d better start hauling her up soon,’ I said.

We shook her up, got the spanker on her, put her close on the wind.

‘I’ll go down and get thawed out now. Keep a good lookout.’ He hurried away.

I stood there looking off into the vapor. I can almost swear I saw a barge go across our stern awhile ago. I smiled to myself and reverently, (for a sailor) whispered: GOD.

I’ll never tell the Skipper about the doings of this night BUT you can see anything in this damn vapor!

Just before daylight I heard the fog-horn of the Cape. It sure sounded good; we knew then we were working our way out of the Bay. The vapor still thick and the wind blowing hard and the old girl looked like an iced-up Christmas tree. The Skipper and I had breakfast together, he couldn’t stop talking about the storm.

‘Last night was about the worst I ever put in at sea; I believe this damn Bay is haunted, he said. Then he lowered his voice, ‘You know what, Bill? I could swear I saw a barge, twice, out there. You’ll think I’m crazy! In one of those hard snow squalls I thought I saw a boat along the lee side with six men in it.' (I smiled to myself and thought—seven,) 'Just between you and me, Bill, I'll never come up this Bay again if they offer me a hundred a ton freight.'

'It's a damn bad place to be anytime, sure hellish on a night like last night,' I said. 'A fellow can see anything in this vapor. There has been a mighty lot of vessels lost in the Bay, generally take all hands with them. I wouldn't be surprised if there was a few 'ghost ships' around.'

'I'll believe anything about this Bay, even 'ghost ships' and 'sea-wolves', the Skipper said.

Davey and Glooscap

A few nights later, Captain Abbott sent for me to come aboard, we were off North Head, Grand Manan. It was as thick as mud, but I got away without being seen by any of the crew.

Captain Abbott's schooner was for fishing. It was of the old style with a round counter. It had six dories nested on deck. When I got aboard, the Captain was in the after cabin.

'Hello, Bill', he said, 'I'm sure glad to see you.' We shook hands. I was some pleased to see him.

'Come on down and sit a spell,' he invited.

When I came aboard, I noticed that she had a whole fore-sail, two head-sails and a storm try-sail on her. The wheelman was on the wheel box having a smoke. There was only a moderate breeze and she was heading toward the southard.

The wheelman said, 'Hello, Bill, don't think you remember me?'

'Yup, I think so', I replied, but, really all those fishermen look alike.

I went down to the cabin. Most of the fishing boats are built alike; one big cabin with underdeck bunks. They generally have a small room forward, on the starboard side, for the Captain. I stopped a minute on the bottom step, until my eyes got used to the light. There were two men in the cabin, both big men but I think Captain Abbott topped the other by a good six inches.

'Well, Bill,' the Captain said, 'Meet Captain Henn.'

'Holy mackeral!' I exclaimed. 'Captain Henn. I've sure heard about you. The hardest sail-dragger and the best fish taker that ever came off the Eastern shore!' My heart thumped with what I had blurted—'But, I thought you was lost with all hands?'

'I was,' Captain Henn said quietly.

'You're forgetting yoursel, Bill', said Captain Abbott.

'I'm sorry, I said, 'But,' humbly, 'how did it happen sir?

'Oh, one of those pig-headed tramp skippers, too mean to blow a whistle in a fog and too lazy to keep a proper lookout. He ran me down in a gale of wind. He should have had his ticket taken away from him and put in jail for the rest of his life. That's the same as murder,' the Captain explained.

'He's been taken care of now,' said Captain Abbott. 'It's been a good many years since that happened. Sit down, Bill, and I'll tell you about the kind of work we do here.'

We all settled back and lit our smokes—they to pipes and me a cigarette.

'Do you remember how you used to talk about unlucky skippers, Bill?' Captain Abbott asked. 'How you used to say they must have had a 'Davey Jones' pilot aboard. And I used to tell you to trust no one. Even after you had made Lurcher Light-ship and it shut down thick and started to blow hard; when your compass, log, charts and tide book didn't seem right—well, I used to tell you to double your lookouts and stay on deck yourself and put your trust in the Lord? But, you'd still insist if you had one of Davey's pilots aboard; you'd play any hunch for safety.

'Well, I used to feel the same way, but I never said anything about it. But, you know, one morning I woke up on board the 'Locker', Jimmy Lido checked me in. After I got my dunnage stowed away, I came on deck and was talking to the watchman. I didn't know any of them. They were all old-timers and hard-boiled but darn fair to their crew. The men, I saw, were clean and looked well-fed and happy and the 'Locker' was spotless.

'Jimmy Lido,' the mate came along and said 'Mister you can go ashore to the Green any time you like,' he laughed and added, 'you won't have to stand a watch for some years and anyway I'll let you know in plenty of time.

'So, I went ashore. Little Mrs. Green is the most beautiful Isle in the world. Everything you want. You know the things we used to wish for? A couple of quarts of good rum and your sweetheart—they all were there. The girls live on part of the Island, by themselves, in beautiful homes. They came to the Fountain—the central meeting place—every day to meet their sweethearts.

'You can have all the rum you want to drink; tobacco to smoke; your meals ashore or on board. The cabin-boys will bring them to you anywhere on the Island. You never ate such cooking! And the cabin boys were so anxious to wait on you!

'But, the solution is very simple. I was there about five years before I found out.

'The chief steward would list the cooks and cabin boys as they came aboard, like Jimmy Lido listed the sailors. The chief steward would tell the cooks they would have to wait their turn to do the cooking; also the cabin boys to wait their turn. You can imagine how happy a good cook was to get a turn, after waiting four or five years. That's how the 'Locker' is run. Aboard you are allowed three grogs a day.

'There is always a regular crew standing watch. Everyone in turn. Your pay starts the day you go aboard. Every ten years you are paid in gold. And another thing—strange as it may seem, you are just in the happiest years of your life and that is the way you stay.

'You'd be surprised at the number of men there over fifty! There is never an ugly word or fight; nor any drunks. Everybody is always happy.

'You can hear some wonderful yarns if you want to sit and listen. I'll tell you them someday.

'Just like other lads, we slick up to go ashore to see the sights and maybe a girl.

'There is one other thing: Remember those thieving skippers that would rob the sailors of their wages; those bulldozing mates that were always looking for the sailors to do? Those belly robbing cooks, too lazy to keep their galley's clean. Those sailors always trying to get work and taking stores aft, when they got a chance? Then, to hear them when they went ashore; what a man they were and neither feared God, man or the devil?

'Well, they never get to the 'Locker'. They are sent off on a barge called the 'Hell Diver'. It's always trying to beat out clear of the Devil's Island. There's a gale of wind in her teeth with rain and snow most of the time. They were ship at every watch, bending new sails and reaving of running gear and fighting among themselves. They tell me there has never been a man ashore since boarding the barge.

'I was around the Green for many years. I saw many men I knew, but, I hardly ever saw a Bay of Fundy Skipper. When I did happen to run across one, I noticed all the others spoke very respectfully to him.

'One day I saw everybody rushing down to the beach, so I went along to see what was going on. There was a small barge coming in the Bay. Boy! She was stepping along. I could hear everyone talking; 'That's Captain Sanford in the Parlo. It would do your heart good to see the way he rounded that barge to and went to anchor, astern of the 'Locker'. Her sails were all furled by the time the anchor touched bottom.

'You wouldn't believe it could be done that smooth, it was the Portuguese skipper talking. What trade is he in?'

'That old man knows his business,' I replied reverently 'He sails out of the Bay, one damn fine man. I've begged to go with him. He's sailed full-rigged ships for forty years.

'I kept looking at that beauty. The style of her was familiar. A skipper I knew from the Gulf of Mexico, took a long breath and said 'Whew! What a beauty. That's a Bluenose or I'll eat my hat. We all laughed as he sure likes the Mexican somberos.

The sailors swung out and lowered a boat just as smoothly as a man-o-war. The Captain, a big man, came down the ladder, got into the boat and was rowed to the 'Locker'.

'Jimmy Lido was in charge. Just before the boat reached the gang way, who came on deck but Captain Davey Jones, himself and stood waiting at the head of the gangway. As that big man came aboard, a great cheer went up. The two Captains shook hands and stood there talking.

'That man is sure well liked,' I said to the skipper.

'Wait till you meet him and you will cheer too,' he replied.

Then the big man shook hands with the other officers, then went to the break of the poop to speak to the sailors. Boy! You should have heard the cheers! He must have promised them a job with him and an extra ration of grog.

'We all started to drift around and talk.

'The crew will soon be abroad and then we'll hear some yarns,' 'Jimmy will send out a crew to place them,' said the skipper.

'I went ashore to the Green and drifted into a pub. Soon in came Captain Hube with Captain Joe.

'Come over here, Bill, and meet the Captain,' called Captain Hube; we all shook hands and had a drink.

'Are you from the little barge?' I asked Captain Joe.

'Little,' laughed Captain Hube. 'Yep! we both were aboard her. Captain Joe—say, you must remember the Captain? Don't you remember five, maybe, six years ago, we went ashore with Captain Joe? He was always in a hurry to get ashore to see his little woman. Remember the time she sent him to town to get some steak for dinner and he fell in with Jerry, you and me? Maybe you don't remember, ha? It was three days before he got home with the steak. The wrapper was off and he had the steak in his hands, smelling. Ye gods! The Little Woman met him at the door with the broom-flailing; she made him bury it. We all had a good laugh over that —later.

'Well, we had another drink and I asked them what they were doing now. They said go see Captain Sanford—

'Captain Sanford?' I exclaimed, 'I know him. That was him that went aboard the 'Locker' a little while ago.

'That's him,' they said in unison, 'and he wants to see you in the morning.'

'I'll be there,' I promised.

'We broke up after a few drinks, then Captain Joe said, 'Well, must go to see the Little Woman.' We laughed for he had the habit of calling them all Little Woman.

'The next morning I went aboard the barge. She certainly was a dandy ship, neat as a pin. Captain Abbott met me.

'Remember when you were aboard before, Bill?' he asked.

'Yes, but it was at night and I didn't get a good look at her.

'She's built of oak and teak and copper sheathed on the bottom. She's the prettiest ship I've been aboard; the best gear and the pick of sailors.' He sure loved the barque!

'Then he took me to the Captain's cabin, knocking said, 'Bill is here.'

'The Captain was at his desk, he had a big log book in front of him. He stood up and shook hands.

'Glad to see you, Bill,' he smiled.

'I was dumb for a minute. This was the same man that remembered me when I was a kid and had talked to me the night of the Bay of Fundy storm.

'Well, Bill, I'm going to tell you something. Your folks told me to keep an eye on you. You see, we were borned and raised in the same place. Although I'm a little ahead of your time, I knew your dad well, through the years we've lost track of each other. He went to the case-oil business to China and thereabouts and I went to the South American trade and sailed to Europe. So, you see Bill, I like to keep track of you. Smoke and tell me what you have been doing.

'I'm sure surprised to see you and when you went aboard the 'Locker', I had a hunch I knew you and the barque—well, I'll never forget her. She was beautiful coming in yesterday.

'Takes one Bluenose to spot another,' he laughed. He called a steward to bring drinks. It sure was swell rum.

'Yes, it's good! Been in the fore peak for some years. I take a drink once in awhile. if I think the malaria is going to get me.

'We sat there, just talking about the old town news and the folks. He said most of his old gang was here—oh, a few didn't make it. They're on the Hell Diver. You know the ones; he didn't mention any names. But, if they were the ones I thought of, well, it was a good (or bad) place for them to be.

'After a time I asked him what trade he was in now. I'm curious. Everyone I ask, just laughs and says to ask you.

'He smiled and said, 'I think you have a pretty good hunch what we do. We are the Bay of Fundy 'pilots'.

'I was on my feet, pleading to go with him. 'Most of my ancestors came to the 'Locker' from there,' I said.

'Sit down, Bill,' he said. 'I'll tell you all about it. We patrol the Bay now, and give warning to all those that will listen. A long time ago, so Captain Davey tells me, when the Indians had charge, they had a Great Chief, who looked after all the trade. The Beavers had built a great dam across it, where Minas Channel is now. The tides weren't so bad then and the Sea Wolves were always trying to destroy everything, if they could eat it or not.

'One time, when the S.W. wind was in a bad mood, it lashed the Bay into a white foam—you've seen it yourself? Well, the Sea Wolves, under the foam, ganged up and tore the dam out, destroyed all the beavers.

'Glooscap, that is the big Chief's name, got sore and he came here to 'Davey' and told him how the wolves were getting the upper hand. He asked 'Davey' to take over.

'Davey' didn't have any men that knew the Bay well, and the Chief would have to let him have some. The Chief agreed and sent him fifty of his best canoe-men.

'The chief said he was going to quit the Bay and come in to 'Davey's Locker.'

'You know that Island—Ile Haute—we anchored behind in times gone by, at the mouth of the Channel? Well, that was his cooking pot, and by gad! he turned it over when he left the Bay.

'It's always stood as a symbol to his faith and courage in keeping the Bay clear for the real Bluenose skippers.'

The Storm

For a long time the MicMacs didn't have much to do. Just look after their own people. The natives didn't pay much attention to them—but, if they went out in their canoes and the Sea Wolves got one of them—then there was a to-do.

After losing a canoe load or two, they came to Davey Jones (chief pilot of Davey Jones' Locker). They were very excited and cried out: 'Captain Davey! a big canoe with wings is in the Bay. What will we do?'

'You are sworn pilots', Captain Davey told them. 'It's your duty to see that they get in and out safely. That is, if they will listen to you.'

As the years rolled on more ships came and the passengers were seeking homes. Some were taken up the best rivers and shown places to build. They thought they were awfully lucky. They never knew about the pilots that escorted them.

Others came to rob and plunder the Indians—all they thought about was murder and loot. Some of these got out of the Bay again but a good many didn't. They landed aboard the Hell Diver and there they remained.

After a hundred years the descendants of those first settlers started to build their own vessels and sail them. Some could speak the MicMac tongue and were mighty glad of the escorting pilots respect.

The ship building went on apace and the young skippers were trading all over the world. However, they always returned home for over-haul, paint and repairs to sails, etc. They would be so anxious to get home, after a long trip, they would take some awful chances in the Bay of Fundy. They would run into a gale of wind and lowering fog, but the war canoes of the MicMacs, with twelve paddlers, would come alongside. The Chief would jump aboard and make signs for the Captain to go back. Some would understand and heave-to, taking an awful beating in the mouth of the Bay, still remain afloat. Others wouldn't listen and kept going, taking in more water trying to run the gale, rain and fog. Generally these were lost, with all hands, in sight of the lights of home. A sad 'home-coming' after a long voyage.

So, in Davey Jones' Locker quite a crew of us were gathered. We called a meeting to ask Captain Davey if we could help with the pilot job.

'Well, boys, I'll have to yarn with Chief Glooscap.'

One day they got together and had a real pow-wow. They came to an agreement and decided to fit out a Barque.

My great-grandfather was the first Captain of the Barque. Through his and the crew's efforts they cut down a lot on the loss of ships and lives. But some of the Captains were careless, would dismiss his warnings as a bad dream. They would always get into trouble. Others believed him and made record runs and a bonus for themselves and the owners.

'I've only been sailing her for forty years,' he told a few of us one day. 'This is my log-book and you are welcomed to read the entries at any time. Every ship that has been in the Bay in the last forty years is recorded there and everything that happened to them.'

I, being the relation, thanked him and then said, 'There are some vessels I would like to know the real facts about.'

'We have a fishing schooner in the mouth of the Bay to keep an eye on the fishermen, and anything else that comes along, when we are busy further up the Bay,' he told us.

'How would you like to sail her sometimes, Bill? he asked me. Was I proud and scared! I always thought I'd have to wait until I learned more.

'But, the other men, older than I?' I asked. But they told me to go ahead.

'Have you forgotten that Davey has your record in his log? It's clean and a few merit marks for saving a life. Every mark counts, Bill.' He smiled and went on: 'There is another man that came out of the Bay. He will be taking over for awhile then I'll send for you.'

That settled we asked him to tell us about some of the ships. 'What about the Anthony? What happened to her, Captain?'

'Well, she was lost about twenty years ago. There was only one man got off her and he was always hazy about what happened. He was pretty badly beaten.' He got up and got the log, leafing over the pages, 'Here it is; was in October, twenty years ago.' He began to read the log: 'Schooner-Anthony; Master—Dan Yates; First mate—Fred Dater; Cook—Sam Samuels; Deck hands—Jim and Mike Doue; (two men short for crew.) Hailed from Bay Port and was on home trip from an American port. Lost in Advocate Bay. Three men to the Locker. Refer to Captain Davey's log for full report.' He looked at me with a half smile.

'I know those particulars well,' he said. 'I put the first pilot aboard her. If you remember anything about Captain Yates, you know he was a very stubborn man. He was born in Norway; came out to the Bay in a Norwegian ship. He hopped her and went aboard a Bluenose. He was smart and a mate at eighteen. Before he was thirty, he was Skipper and part owner of the Anthony, and in the coasting trade.

'He married and had a nice family and home. The years passed and trade was good—and bad. Towards his sixties, trade wasn't so good. Freights were low but he pulled along for a few years then bad luck hit him hard. Mostly he trusted his hunches.

'You know,' the Captain continued, 'when we put a pilot aboard you always have a hunch you were alright. I heard it rumored around that he was getting into debt and the ship brokers were putting it over on him. Likely this would be his last trip as they were planning to take the Anthony from him and getting a younger captain.

'I put a pilot aboard him right after dinner; the day was fine with a light N.W. breeze. But we knew there was going to be hell to pay before morning. It was the mates' watch and the pilot advised him to make Quaco.

'Yates had been lying down after dinner, he got up and came on deck. 'I've a hunch I should make Quaco,' he said, 'The weather looks too good. Everyone would think I was crazy to go in there on a nice day like this.'

'He walked back and forth across the quarter for awhile. He was in socks and very quiet. Jim, the deck-hand was steering and the mate standing by.

'Mister Mate, we'll drive the old girl to the head of the Bay or to—hell.' With those words he turned and went to his cabin.

'The pilot signalled for me to come and take over. 'That Yates!' he said, 'has a stubborn streak on and I can't do anything with him. I overheard him telling the mate that this was his last trip and he would be broke after he paid the crew off; likely lose his ship. He also said that was the reason he was short-handed—no money.

'Well, just about dusk, I put Captain Hube aboard. He's one of the best men in the Bay. They were just abeam of Cape Dor by then; it was about high water and the wind swung S.E. The pilot suggested standing more to the south.

'I've a hunch,' said Captain Yates back on deck and talking to the mate, 'We've better stand to the south, it's going to be a dirty night.' The mate agreed and they talked ships, trips and sailed southard. The wind still light and the tide beginning to ebb.

'The Wolves got to spinning around in whirlpools. They watched their chance and then spun the vessel to the north.

'We'll work her in under Cape Dor and hang on until low water,' Yates said to the mate.

Captain Hube tried everything he knew to stop him from anchoring there. He even spoke to the mate; they were uneasy.

'I don't like the idea of going to anchor there,' said the mate. 'It would be better to go back out into the Bay with the tide.'

'No, by yeases! I'm not going back out into the Bay. I should have made Quaco. I didn't. I'm not going back. I'm going to anchor.'

'They went to anchor about an hour to ebb tide. They hauled the jib down, left the main and fore-sail on her. All went into the cabin where the cook made coffee and set out some food.

'Sam, the cook, was slightly paralaysed on the left side, his arm and leg unsure, but he certainly could get around. He had guts, that Sam! He used to say he could bake, boil, fry or frittle with any damn cook in the Bay of Fundy.

'The pilot listened to them talk; he knew they were doomed but he couldn't do anything about it after they went to anchor.

'They were all uneasy. The mate was on deck every few minutes. When he went back to the cabin, Yates would come out and have a look around. Nobody thought of turning in.

'Half an hour before low water—it struck! From the S.W. ass first, as we say.

'Yates was a thorough sailor and knew the danger he was in. He ordered the main and fore-sail off her and paid out the second anchor. He helped the mate give her chain. She had a long windlass in her and within half an hour she was driving into the storm so bad, she was stealing chain over the windlass, and it held.

'If we don't hit bottom at low water,' the mate said to the cook,' we'll be alright. I think the anchors will hold.

'She struck at low water. The second time she hit bottom the main boom topspan lift parted. The boom came down and cut the life-boat in two, where it swung on the davits.

'The Captain saw it was all up with them then. He and the mate got an overcoat on the cook, helped him forward and lashed him to the poll-post. He told his crew, as they huddled together, they had one chance of getting ashore on some of the wreckage when they broke up. Someone might see them from the shore and try to help.

'The main-mast soon went out of her and took part of the deck with it. The crew were having a bad time to hang on. They were under water most of the time. Somehow the cook got loose from his lashings and a sea was washing him down the port side of the deck. By now, they were all tied to the poll-post by ropes around under their arms with a bowlin in them.

'The Captain threw his off and went after the cook and caught him aft of the fore-riggin's, he hung onto him and the riggin'. The mate slipped out of his lashings to help him. They had a lot of guts; they were going to save the crippled cook or go with him. They had him between them and dragging him back, when the fore-mast went over the side—taking all hands with it.

'They were aboard the Locker in time for breakfast.

'Jim, the deck hand, still hung on to the wreckage. The vessel went to pieces fast after the fore-mast went out of her.

'The pilot signalled for me to come and take him off. I went in the boat myself and I can tell you, fellows, I never saw a worse wreck in my life. She was literally all smashed to pieces.

'The pilot told me he put the sailor on a piece of wreckage—the deck beam—and sent him off, hoping he'd drift ashore. He made it to a little cove, and when able got to the Lighthouse. The keeper was away, but his wife was there. Mike, the other sailor was adrift somewhere out there.

'The Light keeper's wife and Jim went to the tower and at the first streaks of dawn they could see a man adrift. So they took a small boat and went out to try to get him only to be too late.

'She used to tell the tale how that the sailor said he was unconscious but somebody put him ashore. 'Until the day I die, I'll always believe the Locker sent one of their pilots!'

'Jim Doue still goes to sea but he is still hazy about what happened that night.'

The Rips and Storms

The next day we grouped around the Captain again asking him to tell us more of his experiences in the Barque. He got the log out and turned a few pages:

'Here is a sad one,' he said. 'The schooner Klondyke, Captain Jim Kelps and his son, Jimmy. Drowned in Dory Rips. Ever hear about them.' We all nodded then settled down to hear the tale.

'She was a small schooner in the coal trade out of Cumberland Bay to the South Shore. She went down around Cape Chinco.

'The Leno Brothers owned her and the Captain had his only son aboard as mate. The lad was nearing his twenties and as smart as they come.

‘The wind was S.W. and blowing hard so the Captain decided to keep and run up the channel.

‘When he was getting near the Dory Rips, we put a pilot aboard and told him to get his ship snugged up as there was a hell of a sea in the Rips.

‘He had just lowered the main-sail about half way down but hadn’t reefed it. We knew if he didn’t get his ship snugged up he was going to take an awful beating.

‘He hung on until he was in sight of the Rips and could see the hellish tide running there. Then they tried to take the main-sail in and reef it.

The boy got the foot ropes on the main boom to hook the reef tackle on. He had just taken a pull on it when the foot rope parted and he dropped over the stern. He hung onto the hauling part of the tackle. His father jumped on the boom, crawled out to grab the tackle and haul the boy back aboard.

‘The sailor at the wheel ran to help the Captain get down on deck again, holding onto the rope until the Captain could take it again. He had to get to the wheel again—the ship was nearing the Rips.

‘The father got the boy almost to the taffrail when a sea buried her, nearly taking the Captain with her. When he pulled the rope in, as the ship came up out of the sea, the boy was gone.

‘The father stood up—speechless! The sailor took one look then turned away. There was nothing to be done.

‘I ordered the pilot to try taking the ship through the Rips safely. She got a terrible washing but they made it.

'Those two men never knew, until they got to the 'Locker' how they made the trip through the Rips.'

Captain Abbott and I talked idly about the happenings of the past. He was turning the leaves of the log, looking up at me, said: 'Here's one the Captain of the Barque should remember well. Bet you too, have heard the old folks talk about it.

So, we all turned to the Captain where he sat at his desk, said 'We would like to hear that story, sir.

'Well, that was some trip,' the Captain sighed. 'It was the schooner Thema. Captain Thompson and a crew of seven. Mate Olsen, a good man; second was Levede; three Norwegians for deck hands; a Finn before the mast and a black cook.

'She was loaded with barrel plaster from Hillsboro and took on a deck load of lathes at Shulee.

'Yes,' I butted in, 'we've all heard about the trip but never the details.'

'Then listen, boy,' said the Captain, 'and you will hear all about what happened. She disappeared in a N.E. gale and took all hands with her.

We moved into a closer circle around the Captain where he leaned back in his chair. He seemed upset about this tale but could see we were all anxious to hear it.

'Well,' began the Captain, 'Capt. Thom—as he was known—came in the Bay in the Fall with a load of hard coal.

He planned on picking up a load of potatoes for Cuba and getting a quick turn around and be out of the Bay with another load before bad weather set in.

'He didn't bother to charter her in New York as he and the agent Harris were personal friends, and he was always sure of a load. So he just sent him a wire saying he would be in the Bay on such and such a date and then forgot about it.

'He came up the Bay to the little village where he lived, unloaded, then beached so he could copper-paint the bottom. This done, he wired Harris that he was ready to load most anytime.

'Well, a wire came back saying Mr. Harris had died and after the funeral he would get his orders.

'Mr. Harris was one of those old time business men—shrewd but honest. He would look you over and if you passed his judgment, he would take your word before your note. He wasn't much for lawyers and most of his business was 'word of mouth'; so you see things were in an awful mess when he passed away.

'He must have hundreds of barrels of potatoes spoken for from farmers and a lot of them had drawn on him for advances; others had delayed in getting their money until delivery.

'Harris hadn't married until he was along in years, and his oldest boy was only seventeen. The widow was left with all these verbal agreements, many of them her husband had forgot to mention. The lawyers wanted her to give them permission to check each and every vessel her husband had been interested in.

'But she said, 'No. Mr. Harris wouldn't wish it; he trusted them and they did him. I don't understand the chartering of vessels. The brokers in Halifax and St. John will see to that part. In a year or so, when the boy is older, he will be able to help me.

'After a week of waiting, Capt. Thom found out he couldn't get a load; the brokers could charter 'bottoms' cheaper than he could take them. So he wired New York office if they had anything and word came there was a load of barrel plaster in Hillsboro but the freight was low. He took it and also a chance for a deck load of lathes; with the two he could about clear expenses.

'It was late in the Fall by now, and the lathes were covered with snow and ice when he got them on deck and lashed down.

'He knew there was going to be a blizzard as the glass was falling and the wind N.E. He was anxious to get out of the Bay. It was just dark when they cleared the harbour; she had all her lower sail on her.

'She had a steam donkey boiler in her and a good crew. He figgered he'd get out of the Bay by next forenoon and then he'd heave to. He was out about an hour when the blizzard struck with a blinding snow storm. But her sail and gear was good and he dragged her on something cruel.

'We put a pilot aboard as soon as she went out and told him to short her down and go out the North channel.

'Capt. Thom told the mate—'I've a hunch I should go out the North channel but I'm going out the South so heave her along as soon as she is clear. We'll leave the spanker on her as long as we can.'

'Before nine she got to steering so bad they had to slack it down some in the jacks. He told the mate to try to carry it until midnight, then take it in and tie up.

'They both had been on deck since they came aboard. About eleven the Capt. went to his cabin; in a few minutes he came back and called the mate to come down; that left the second in charge. The Finn was steering and there was a man on lookout forward, but, you couldn't see the length of her in that blinding snow.

'When the mate went into the cabin the Capt. had a chart spread out on the table. His souwester was off and his glasses perched on his nose.

'Well, son,' he said to the mate, 'I've a queer hunch we're not going out of the Bay as fast as we think. Maybe we had better run her off another point. I don't think we are giving Quaco Ledges room enough.

'We'll go up, keep her off a point and tie up the spanker as the sea is getting bad awfully fast.

'Alright, sir,' said the mate and turned towards the door. Before he could get it opened, the ship ran down in one of those big seas and struck a sharp reef. The bottom went out of her and she never came up—just slid off and went down like a stone. They never got out of the cabin.

'The lookout had just stepped towards the fo-castle to tell his mates to put lots on as it was hellish cold on deck,— he never made it. They didn't last ten minutes in that sea.'

'The Captain of the Barque sighed again, then said— 'That's the sea for you! Well, boys, how about a drink?

'We all agreed and set about, idly, talking about those Ledges and how scared we were of them.

'It pays to be afraid of them,' the Captain said. 'It pays to be.'

'We sat there smoking and talking. I picked up the log and saw a name: Schooner Hattie MacKay. I knew that name well and turning to the Captain of the Barque said, 'Will you tell us about the Hattie MacKay, sir?

'To-morrow, Bill, maybe to-morrow. Better get busy now.

'With a chorus of 'Aye, Aye, sir,' we went our separate ways.

The Final Analysis

'It was a lovely, fine day as we gathered on the deck of the Barque and Captain Sanford was in good spirits. He liked to spin a yarn even though some of them made him sad. The bye-gone days were great days filled with life and daring. Greater risks were taken and as he remarked the sailors of to-day were 'molly-coddled.'

He turned the pages of the log and there it was: Hattie MacKay. Master: Captain Cordy. Cook: his wife Amanda. Mate: his son Willy. Crew: Nicknamed Do and Don't. (I think their names were Donald and Darrel Willets.)

'The Hattie MacKay!' he said, 'eighty tons registered.' He closed the log and looked at us, 'I can tell you about her without the log.' He sighed.

'Captain Cordy had loaded coal up the Bay for Black's Harbour. It was late in the Fall and had a good run out and discharged. Then he had a chance to get a load of weir poles for somebody on the South Shore.

'When he told his wife about it she wanted him to go to St. John for a load of freight. They talked it over, the three of them.

'We got power in her,' said the son. They had two small but good engines. They decided to dodge over to the South Shore then make for St. John.

'But, I think they loaded at St. George, making good time and getting right out. They had a big deck load, too much for that time of year, but they were depending more on the engines than sail.

'When they came out past the 'Wolfs', I sent a pilot aboard her to tell the Captain to turn back or go into Beaver Harbour, as there was going to be a gale soon.

The wind was light and S.W. and as he had the engines going, he was walking right along.

'When he went down to dinner he said to his wife, 'I think we ought to make Beaver Harbour. If we were in sail I would go in but with those damn engines—' He didn't finish what he had in mind. His wife was worried when she heard him swear for he was a religious man.

'But, he kept the engines going and made six or seven knots an hour. When he went back on deck Willy was steering. (Willy wasn't their real son, they had taken him when he was a baby and now never doubted he belonged to them.)

'Captain Cordy said to him, 'The wind is hauling to the eas'ward; it will blow a gale soon.

'Not very good for us but fair wind for someone,' said Willy.

'After awhile the Captain's wife came on deck, said everything was snug below and she'd steer for awhile; Willy could keep an eye on her. 'You get some sleep, Captain, if it blows tonight you'll be on deck. I baked a birthday cake—you're celebrating tomorrow.

'She was seventy and he seventy-four and tomorrow she would tell him this was their last trip.

'He went to the cabin. She told Willy to get some coal for the galley stove. She knew the compass course and as good at a trick of steering.

'Do, the sailor was down keeping an eye on the engines, he was uneasy but driving them hard.

'The Captain came back on deck—he too, was uneasy when he heard the pilot's warning.

'I think we ought to turn back,' he said to his wife.

'What's wrong with you today? You go right back and lay down. We'll be under the South Shore by ten o'clock.' But she was uncertain too, for they were depending on those engines to get them there.

'It was just about dark; the son was having his supper, when there was a crash in the engine room. He ran to see what had happened; a connecting rod had broken and came out through the block. He and Do shut the engine off then came up on deck. They were pretty white and scared but the son went back to his supper. He told his mother they couldn't fix it until they got ashore.

'That's alright, son,' she said. 'The Captain said he would reef all around, for we won't be able to beat up the South Shore with full sail. We've too big a deck load,' she sighed, 'Guess I'll do the dishes.'

'Willy went on deck; the Captain was at the wheel and Don't was lowering the mainsail. He gave him a hand; the wind was still easterly.

'Mrs. Cordy came on deck and gave the boys a hand—she had to do something, 'keep busy' her mind said, 'keep busy.' The son pulled out the reef tackle, passed and repassed the earing, she and Don't passed the tack lashings and tied reef points. When they had the single reef in they decided to double reef her, while they had it down and it was still smooth.

'So they slapped a double reef in and set it. They lowered the foresail and put a double reef in it; they took the standing jib in and tied it up. The wind went S.E. and started to breeze up. The Captain let her go close-hauled on the starboard. She was heading E by N.

The Captain was hoping that on the turn of the tide she would cut in under the shore. But it started to breeze up harder, the wind and now driving snow hauled her to the eastward and the sea was making fast.

'It was getting on to nine—everything was snugged up and they were sure of their vessel—but the big deck load worried them.

Do had some life in one engine but it was never made for the work it was doing now. The vessel made a rouse in the sea. There was a wild racing in the engine; Willy went below and shut it off. They came on deck and put on oil-skins. They were very worried and Do told Willy he thought one of the propellers was gone.

'Don't you worry, son,' said his mother, 'this old boat can run like a scared dog.'

'We'll keep off and run back,' the Captain said to his son. 'We ought to be able to make somewhere at daylight.' He didn't want the boy to think he was worried.

'He kept her off as much as he could but the wind went N.E. and a blinding blizzard set in. Like the Mrs. had said the old Hattie MacKay could run like a scared dog but she had had her day. She started to leak like a seive!

'They started the pump but it took all its power to keep her free. The Captain slipped the brake on the hand pump; he and Willy were pumping by spells to help the engines to keep a suck on her.

He tied a rope around Willy making one end fast to the mast for the seas were very high now and an extra big one would fill the pump well full. They were both soaking wet and it was bitter cold. They knew they had to keep the water out of her or they were done.

'At the wheel the old Captain was putting up his last fight; drawing on his sixty years experiences and using every ounce of it. He would ease her into a sea, like a mother laying her babe in a crib. He knew she was going too fast; he dared not take the mainsail in before he tried for North Head or shelter somewhere. He really didn't know where he was.

'She was a sturdy boat; She would bury up forward and once in awhile a sea would board her amidship.

'Down in the galley—it was now midnight—Mrs. Cordy had her dishes washed and everything made as snug as possible in the wild pitching of the vessel. The tea kettle was lashed to the stove and the coffee was in the rack-steaming, she was going to serve coffee to all.

'She was standing, hanging onto the table to keep her feet. An old, grey-headed woman. She seemed to be in deep thought but suddenly she straightened to full height and smiled to herself.

'She wet the corner of a towel and wiped her face, then combed her hair, then went to the Captain's cabin. There she took off her working clothes and dressed in her best. Her silk shirt waist and the skirt she saved for Sunday church going. Then over these a sweater and oil-skins, lastly her rubber boots. She knelt down by the bunk and said a prayer, then getting up and steadying herself, she looked around that wildly rolling cabin saying 'Good bye.'

'She went up on deck bracing herself against the wind and getting used to the nights' darkness. She went to the Captain at the wheel and asked if he was cold. 'No dear,' he said. He could see her smile from the reflection of the binnacle light.

'She worked around to the lee side of the wheel and took hold of it with him; she patted the firm old hands that gripped the spokes so tightly. He nodded and she could see a ghost of a smile on his lips altho his beard was ice-encrusted.

'She whispered 'Willy?' and then 'Do and Don't?' A question but not a question—a soft whisper.

'The Captain held her hand—'Only us, now.'

'She hadn't been there long when the vessel ran down a big sea; when she started to climb the next one a squall hit her.

The mainsail blew out of the bolt ropes and disappeared in the driving wind and snow. He reached over and patted her shoulder and said: 'We'll weather this.' Both knew they wouldn't—she struck at two o'clock!

A notice appeared in the Shipping Bulletin:

'Schooner: Hattie MacKay. Captain Steven Cordy and his wife, Amanda; son Willy and deck-hands Donald and Darrell Willets. All hands lost.'

Pete Leslie

Pete Leslie was a Bay of Fundy sailor when I knew him some forty years ago. The beach and old wreckage was his play ground and almost his school. He used to boast that a hundred and thirty boats sailed from Kidtown in his youth. There were eleven bars doing full swing business. Of course, the bars weren't all legal.

He was a six-footer, dark complected with snapping black eyes and weighed around a hundred and ninety.

It's funny when I think of him now; he was everybody's friend but no one really knew him. I think I was the only one he really was serious with, then he wouldn't say much and I'd guess the rest.

When I met him, he was about twenty to my thirteen. He was mate of the schooner Adonis; they were loading lumber in West St. John. I was a fresh kid—never been on a boat in my life; I asked him if he wanted to hire 'a man?' I remember he looked me all over with a big grin.

'Will your folks let you go?' He asked still grinning.

'I ain't got any,' I choked. 'I stay with Granny.'

'Oh, I see!' His grin was compassionate, (know that now). 'Well, tell your Granny to give you all the warm clothes you have and a couple quilts.'

You had to carry your own bedding in those days. When I told Granny about him and going to sea, she seemed pleased. It was three or four months before I found out there were thousands of brash kids like me, wanting to go to sea. I sure was lucky to be picked by him.

So I signed on the next day—we were loaded by then and bound for New York—I'll never forget: after I came on board from signing on, he called me aft where we were alone.

'Look youngster! there are a few things I want to tell you. I'm Mister to you when you speak to me on board.

I sorta cringed, 'Yes,' I said.

'Yes, what?' He said it in such a way my heart fell right into my boots.

'Yes, s-sir,' I stuttered in a whisper.

'Good. That's two things you have learned. Now go forward and give the crew a hand,' he ordered, 'The tug will be here at high tide.'

Just before the tug came, I noticed the rest of the crew looking up the wharf and laughing. There was Pete! His arms around one of the swellest looking dames I've ever seen. She had both arms around his neck and I think she was crying.

One of the older hands said, 'I don't know how in hell he does it. I've been with him over a year and it's the same where-ever we go.'

I don't remember much more of that night and the next day. I was too sick but every four hours I was expected to stay on deck; then I would high-tail it for the bunk. They call it mal-de-mer but I call it plain hell.

I found out later that this was a new schooner and her first trip. The Captain's name was Newbe. He and Pete were a hard boiled pair and they were some proud of their command.

We came out of St. John in a S.W. gale into the Bay. All the Captain would say—'We're out here and when the wind shifts it's got to be for the better. It couldn't blow from a worse quarter.

After a few days I was eating my meals and getting around pretty good. Pete would ask me if I thought I was going to 'live.'

'Yes, sir,' I'd assure him, 'I'm alright now.' He kept me working all my time on deck. He showed me how to 'seize on rattlin' then he would come to take a look at what I had done.

'Is that the way I showed you?' he'd ask.

'Yes, sir, only I put a few more turns around,' I'd answer.

'Take them all off and put them on the way I showed you and,' he looked at me without a smile, 'don't you go below before the job is finished.'

My watch was just about up; I knew he meant what he said. After he went aft, I began to think fast and furious: 'Hell! It's going to take all my free time off to change them.' Still swearing I set to work; after this I would do what I was told.

We made the run to City Island in less than a week; we towed from there up to the Brookline side in New York to a lumber yard, and started to discharge cargo. We did most of the stevedoring ourselves in those days.

It was Saturday before I got shore leave. The mate promised us some money and no work until Monday. It didn't take us long to get going.

I was ready but I didn't like to go ashore alone and besides I didn't have any money coming to me. Of course I was broke and Granny couldn't give me any money before I signed up. I was sitting on my bunk, feeling pretty blue, when the fo'c'sle door slid open and Pete stuck his head in. 'Come along, Bill, let's go ashore,' he said.

I jumped up like a pleased pup—'We'll give this town the once over!' he grinned, 'Ashore my name is Pete.'

'Yes, sir,' I was flustered.

'No, No!' he said, 'that is for aboard ship. I'm Pete and you're Bill when we are on the loose.'

'Yes, Pete,' I said, feeling quite the man.

We went ashore; I strutted—wasn't I with the Mate of the Adonis? He bought ice cream and fizz for me and a drink for himself; he gave me two dollars to buy overalls, also got soap, towels and other things a sailor needs and, needling me, asked if I needed a razor?

We were walking around the counters in a big store; I noticed all the sales-girls had a big smile for Pete. At one counter the girl was a pippin and Pete said, 'Hi Cherrie!' just as though he knew her all his life—'Me and my shipmate are looking for some things to take aboard.'

She gave him a smile that would have knocked you like an anchor—'I think we have anything you need in this store.'

'Now, you wouldn't be included, would you?' It must have been about fifteen minutes before they got through parrying with each other. I know I wormed around and came back before she noticed there was quite a line-up at her counter.

'I'll be back,' Pete said and we went to buy needles, thread and some hankies for me. He kept an eye on her counter, soon as she wasn't busy, we went back.

'Give Bill whatever he wants while I get some socks,' he told her. He was hardly out of ear-shot before she started firing questions at me—'What's his name and what does he do?'

I was proud to answer: 'Why, his name is Mr. Leslie; he's the Mate of our ship the Adonis. She's a brand new one.' I took a deep breath. 'It's my first trip and he brought me ashore with him. He's a great guy! He bought me ice-cream and fizz and all I could eat and drink; he bought me overalls and all this stuff. We're pals when we are ashore; I only have to say 'Sir' when we are on board.' I tried to impress on her the grandness of this,

She smiled at me, said: 'I knew he was a great guy, too.'

She might have said more but Pete came back, saying, 'All aboard for supper, Bill.' He looked at her, 'How about tonight?'

'I'll be through about seven, this is stock taking night,' she answered.

'I'll be here,' and from the way she looked at him, I knew she'd be waiting.

When we were on the sidewalk, I blurted, 'Gee, Pete, she's pretty, ain't she? Prettier than the one in St. John.

'Italian girls are all good looking,' he said, 'guess we'll celebrate with a beer.'

I didn't see him again until the next day, Sunday. Around noon he came forward, said, 'How about going to Coney Island this afternoon? I see you've got yourself polished up so I don't think my girl will mind a couple swell lookers.' I knew he was 'rubbing' me.

I had given myself a good slicking up with the nice smelling soap; I was so pleased with the idea that I nearly busted my new overalls. No one had ever bothered with me before!

We went up the street to meet the girl—her real name was Martha—she was on the corner, waiting. When she saw me she smiled and said, 'I knew you would bring Bill.' She got between us and we linked arms. My heart turned a dozen summersaults; she felt so nice and warm. We boarded a trolley—I'll never forget that day, Pete took us through all the amusement places he could find. I knew that every chance he got, he kissed her more than once when we were going through the tunnel in a boat. Then they would remember me—she'd smile and I thought everything was just great!

I ate so much candy, hot-dogs and drank fizz and saw more things than I ever expect to see again. The crowds, pushing and shoving, made me sick and dizzy.

Pete looked at me, then said to Martha, 'Guess we'd better get bathing suits and go to lay down for awhile. I think Bill is getting pretty tired.'

They got bathing suits, but I didn't want one. I swear they were the best looking couple on the beach. She only weighed about a hundred-five and built like a yacht—everything slick and trim in the right places. Pete was like a Bluenose fisherman, clean cut lines and built for all kinds of weather.

We found a place, after some searching, where we could sit down. They told me to stay there as they were going to swim. I guess I fell asleep. I was pretty sick from eating all that stuff; riding miles on the merry-go-round, ferris wheel and scenic railways and a lot of things I didn't know the name of. When I woke up the sun was just setting. Pete and Martha were buried in the sand and having a good time teasing each other, then kissing to make up. To hear Martha laugh was like a silver bell tinkling inside you. It made me feel good all over to see them so happy.

After awhile they got dressed and then we had hamburgers and coffee. Then we walked along the board walk, arm-in-arm, the three of us so close among all those thousands of others. Martha would squeeze my arm and smile at me; I would blow up like a balloon, my eyes must have told her how swell I thought she was.

We took a trolley to the City and we sure had fun; they teased me some but not enough to hurt my feelings. When we got there they walked me down to the lumber yard so I wouldn't get lost. When she said 'good-night' and before I knew it, she put her arms around me and kissed me. I was away like a scared rabbit. I never been kissed by a girl before!

The next day we got the deck load off and started to break out the cargo in the hole. Pete worked along with the rest of us and would buy the 'growler' of beer in his turn. I used to go ashore to get it and the crew would kid me about being out so late the night before, said I must have a girl. I didn't mind. I never told where Pete and I was on Sunday. He didn't tell me not to but I had a hunch he never wanted me to tell anything. I sassed them back and we were all good friends.

We worked all week; Pete wanted to get unloaded by Saturday but we didn't make it.

Martha came down about every day, sometimes at noon but mostly in the evenings. It was my job to get the ladder overside to help her aboard. The crew all swore she was the best 'looker' that Pete even had bets that he was a 'goner' this time. I used to call her Martha when we were alone but aboard she was Miss to all of us. She got a great kick out of it. Some nights we would have a party and I'd go ashore for ice-cream, cake, fizz and candy and I was always the 'white-haired' boy.

By now I could find my way around within two or three blocks from the lumber yard and also to the store where Martha clerked. So, Saturday afternoon I asked Pete if I could go to a show.

'Sure,' he said, 'here's a couple bucks—watch out for that kid gang ashore. Walk along and mind your own business and they'll not bother you. They are as tough as hell in this district.'

I thought I'd be all right as I was raised with a tough gang in St. John. I had a great time that afternoon as I picked up a couple kids (my size) and took them along. They came back to the lumber yard with me but I told them they weren't allowed on board. We planned to meet the next day on the corner, at noon.

So I told Pete I was going ashore and he said, 'Alright son.' That made me feel pretty good; I swaggered through the lumber yard, stopped for a chat with the watchman. Outside the gates I looked for the kids I was to meet, but, the only ones there were some tough looking mugs—and they were tough! They gave me the 'once-over' then started for me. My swagger was gone—I didn't know to run or stand pat!

I looked around for a means of escape and in the lumber yard I saw Pete coming. He was in his shirt sleeves and hat tilted to one side. I walked (scared stiff) slowly towards him. Then one of the thugs yelled, 'Let him have it.' I ducked and ran but Pete came on taking the barrage of sticks and stones meant for me.

He hit out once, twice and two of them went down; a third guy—bigger than the rest—flourished a black-jack and hit at Pete viciously. Pete hit him from a leaning position—I never saw anyone do that before—the black-jack went flying and the tough landed head over heels.

There must have been seven or eight in the gang and did they go for Pete. One got a board and swung at him and the blow took him on the shoulder, he went to his knees. When he straightened up did he flail those lads! But one grabbed a piece of paving stone and flung it, catching Pete in the ribs.

I guess I was too scared to do anything except holler, 'Run, Pete, Run!' A gathering crowd was screeching, 'Fight! Fight!'

Then a woman screamed! Martha came through that crowd like a wildcat. I heard her say in English, 'You dirty bums!' Then she switched to Italian. It must have scorched them for they cowed away, muttering.

She had her arms around Pete—he was pretty wobbly. Then someone yelled: 'Cops!' Those boys knew their stuff; they broke that crowd in a jiffy. The first fellow Pete hit was still out cold; so they took him but the others got away.

Martha was crying now but her eyes were like stars behind the tears and she was crooning—Pete, my Pete! Have they hurt you?'

He was shaking his head but every time he breathed he would wince. Then the police ambulance arrived; the doctor took one look at the tough where the cop guarded him. 'He'll be alright but what about you?' Turning to Pete, he gave him a going over. 'Well, a couple ribs broken. What did they hit you with?'

'Paving stone,' I butted in, 'that fellow there. I saw him throw it.'

They bandaged Pete at the ambulance; said he'd be all right in a few days. The cops asked a lot of questions—'Down Easterner?' they asked him.

'Bluenose,' he said and you know he was proud to be one. He and Martha started for the ship but I hung back, thinking maybe they'd rather be alone.

The cop said to me, 'See the fight?'

'Yes, sir. He's the greatest guy in the world.' I boasted.

'I'll tell you something, son,' he said. 'If they'd got him down he'd be in the morgue by now.'

'Would they have killed him?' I was frightened for I knew Pete had saved me.

'They sure would have and it wouldn't have been the first one, either,' he told me and added—'Someone must have hired them to beat him up like that. That gang don't work for fun; likely that dame is the cause of it all. They must have thought him an easy mark or they'd used knives.' He looked around, 'Sure must have been some fight—two down and three to go.'

'He had three of them down before they hit him with the stone,' I said.

'Well, you had better go aboard and I advise you to stay there,' he told me.

Pete and Martha were nearing the schooner and if I ran I could be at the ladder to help Martha aboard. Pete was teasing her, calling her Little Wildcat and calling her Tom Sharkey the second and saying Cherrie in a way that made the scared look go off her face. It wasn't long before they were laughing. Then they teased me and made me blush.

Just before we got aboard Pete said to me—'I got hit by a car, just bruised some and will be alright in a day or two.'

I caught on quick. 'Why that's too bad, sir. I'll tell the crew.'

After supper Pete sent for me to come to his cabin. He told me to let the crew know he'd had a tip we might get a visit from the river 'pirates' that night and two had better stand watch and have belaying pins handy. Said if anyone suspicious came aboard to hit first and ask questions afterwards.

At eleven I was to get one of the crew to go with me to the watchman's shanty and call a taxi for Martha. He gave two dollars to give the watchman to tell the driver to come through the yard to the ship.

The crewman knew there was something wrong and tried to pump me, but I knew nothing. They were trying to find out if Pete has been jumped. Mike, a Russian Finn, sharpened his sheath knife; big Jim Hyde just stretched his arms—he was a Bluenose, too, and could lick his weight in wildcats. Oscar, a Swede, had a piece of flexible steel wire about two feet long with a 'servin' on each end of it. He was making a loop to go around his wrist. When I saw the wire and all the preparations, I shivered. I knew it would cut anyone to pieces and do more damage than a belaying pin or knife.

The crew thought the world of Pete. They would grouse and growl and kick about everything, as all crews do, but I believe to this day, they would have fought to death for him. I could feel it right there in the fo'castle, that night, when they went quickly about getting ready.

Just before eleven the cook called me and I went to the galley where they'd had coffee. Pete was helping Martha with her coat. She'd been crying but put on a smile for me and said, 'I want you to take good care of Pete for me. Be sure to come to see me on your next trip. Pete has my address.' She put her arms around me and gave me a kiss. I didn't try to get away this time, she felt so nice. Pete grinned, 'Martha,' he said solemnly,' I do believe Bill is going to be an old flirt!'

'Now Pete, you take good care of my Billie.' There were tears in my eyes when I slipped away to go to the shanty. I wasn't used to much kindness.

The crew was all standing by when the taxi came. Big Jim and the Swede were on the wharf, one on each side of it. The Finn was near the ladder, leaning careless like, but I knew he was watching those lumber piles like a cat. The cook came from the galley and I think he had a meat cleaver under his apron.

Pete said good-bye to Martha and I helped her down the ladder, we shook hands (no kissing there!) I told the driver Martha's address; was he a hard-boiled guy as he said out of the side of his mouth: 'I see youse guys are all set for trouble.' We all were silent.

I guess I was the only one that slept that night when I woke up at daylight the crew were eating. We finished unloading before noon and then the Captain came aboard, pretty soon we were underway. We towed to Perth Amboy to take on a load of hard coal, then towed to City Island; we made sail before the tug let go.

The Captain came forward to give us a hand in Pete's place, while he was aft talking to the pilot. I never saw our Captain working before. He seemed to be always dressed up and smoking a big cigar. I thought it must be great to be a Captain! But, he turned out to be almost as good a man as Pete—(no one could come up to Pete in my mind.)

The pilot was set off and the tug let us go; we set our jib and we're away. The Captain sent a man to the wheel to take Pete's place, two more to coiling rope and fixing gear, and then he said to me—'Bill, you and I will stand this watch together.'

Until Pete's ribs knitted, Big Jim, or I, was in the Captain's watch. Big Jim kept telling me he bet the Captain would 'larn' me to steer. Sure enough, on the third watch together, the Captain called me aft. I started to go on the windward side, but, he sent me back to come up on the leeward and come around him to take the wheel. He showed me a black line and a diamond on the compass and said, 'Keep those two together.'

I thought I caught on pretty quick; the wind was fair and light and she steered like a yacht. The Captain didn't have much to say except once he asked me if I saw Pete when he was hit by the car.

I replied, 'Yes, sir.' He didn't ask me anything more so I kept silent. I had a hunch he would give ten dollars to know what really happened. He wouldn't question and I wouldn't 'up and tell' unless Pete said I could.

It was nearly six weeks before I got back on Pete's watch. We had discharged at Yarmouth, then went to St. Mary's Bay for a load for Boston. I was getting round ship pretty good by now. We worked out of St. Mary's Bay, the wind S.W. and light; I was steering the twelve to four watch. 'Dead man's watch,' they call it. Pete was leaning against the wheelhouse and Big Jim was talking to him. Soon he went below, tomorrow was another day.

'Do you ever hear from Martha, sir?' I asked.

'No, Bill,' he answered me so seriously that I was surprised. 'You see, Martha's father has lots of money; he owns two or three fruit stores. Besides,' he said quietly, 'the old fellow has a friend and there is a son that is to marry Martha. All in an Italian family.' 'He kinda jeered at himself—'Italian fruit stores and a combination of son and daughter. They, the two geezers, will retire and dance fat bambinos on their fat knees.' He grinned, 'Martha got sore. She wants to be American and pick her own husband; so she got a job just to show her old man she could make a living. That is where I got fooled, Bill, I thought her just another dame. It took nearly the whole week before she told me about herself and asked me to meet her father.

'Well, when she took me to one of the swankiest places in Brookline, it was more than I expected. It was a swell home and when Martha introduced me to her father, I could see I wasn't wanted around there.

'But, he sure was nice to me; you'd thought I was a visiting royalty. Martha's mother was dead and she an only child. He doted on her but he planned keeping Martha and his money Italian.'

So the upshot of it all was, Pete had told Martha he would not be seeing her again. She had come to the ship that Sunday and that was the reason for the fight. She had told her father she was going to marry Pete and he was furious. He sent for the friend and the son—but, even they couldn't beat Pete!

When she saw the gang jump Pete, she knew her father meant business. Pete didn't care for all the Italians in Brookline come alone or in gangs—He asked Martha to marry him. She wouldn't. Said they would kill him the first opportunity they got and she couldn't face that. Her father belonged to a secret society and had a lot of power among the Italians.

'Oh well, I expect she is married by now.' He shifted his position.

It was nearing four, my trick about over. I had been doing a lot of thinking and said, kinda easy like—'Pete, I bet the first bambino will be named Pete.'

He straightened up and grinned, kinda pleased—'Forget it, Bill.' He started to pace the deck. Big Jim came to relieve me. But, Pete was still pacing when I went below.

On Getting A Wife

Did I ever tell you about the time I stole a woman? I didn't steal her for myself but for the Skipper of the ship I was the mate of.

It was an American schooner and I joined her in New York; we loaded her with hard coal for a small town in Nova Scotia.

After we discharged cargo the Skipper decided to go on the beach to copper-paint her bottom as it would save him a big drydock bill back home. Any clean beach is a drydock in N.S. as the tide drops as much as sixty feet in the Bay of Fundy.

The Skipper got in tow with a woman—she was a good looker! She was married but her husband was a boozer and they didn't get along so good. But she wanted to go to N.Y. with the Skipper; only thing, you couldn't get a clearance with a woman on board unless she was crew, or wife. She didn't want her husband to know she was leaving him.

So, after we got the painting done, we loaded a cargo of lumber for N.Y.—we planned what to do.

The plan was to tow down the Bay to the first sheltered cove and anchor; so we moved out on the noon tide. I was to stay behind with the ship's boat till the later tide and, on the ebb, pick up the woman and her baggage then run down to the schooner with the tide.

I, being young and eager to stand in with the Skipper, didn't realize what I was up against or I never would have tried it. There is one hell of a tide, flood or ebb, in that Bay!

Around the hotel that afternoon, I told the gang I was waiting for some ship stores to come in on the train from Halifax. They asked me if I was going to make the run at night? 'If the stores come in, I guess I will, I replied.

'You're crazy!' An old wharfer told me.' You don't know the Bay well enough and won't get two miles before you are on a sand bar. You'll drown as 'sure as hell'.

Then they told me some wild yarns; I thought they were trying to scare me. They said they wouldn't run the Bay for any money! Some said they 'might' try it with a good shad boat with four men if it was a bright moonlight night. 'Maybe,' I thought, 'the stores wouldn't come.' But—there was the woman!

After supper I went out and picked up a girl. We met the Skipper's woman on the street. I sent the girl to buy some candy so I could get a chance to talk to her.

'My baggage is packed and I'm ready to go,' she said,

'O.K.' I said, 'I'll be around about eleven-thirty; be high near twelve. We'll just about make it from your place to the boat by that time.'

I took the girl home about ten-thirty, promised to see her the next morning; then went along to the hotel and had a few drinks with the night man.

'Guess I'll go down to the wharf to see about my boat,' I told him. 'See you later,' I winked at him, 'Got my eye on a new dame.'

'Knew there was something in the wind,' he grinned in answer. 'You shed the other one mighty early! I'll leave a night light in the office—guess you know your way around.'

I took a roundabout way to the woman's house. She was ready, so I histed her baggage onto my back. I swear it weighed a ton. She must have had everything in it but the kitchen sink!

She went ahead and we took all the short-cuts we could but no one was about. Thank heavens! Everyone goes to bed early in those small towns. It was nearly twelve before we got that damn baggage down to the wharf and she had to help stow it aboard.

The tide was on the turn and by the time we pulled away the ebb was running strong. I just used one oar to scull and steer with; the night was still and black. (If you were ever around the water then you would know that some nights the land looks black. Deep. Lonesome and my God, is it Black!

After awhile there was a few stars a long ways away, and not a breath of wind. I have often thanked God for that!

I knew the tide ran pretty fast in the Bay. The Skipper and I had talked to the longshoremen that loaded us. They said it was no trouble for a fishing boat to go down to the tail of the bar with the tide on ebb; that would be about three or four miles down and in daylight.

We figgered on a six knot tide and the Skipper planned to anchor as far out from the cove as the tug-boat Captain would let him. Our plan should give us plenty of time to make it.

Maybe you have never seen one of those sculling boats? Old-timers and generally about sixteen foot keel, broad of beam and a draught of ten to twelve inch on them; they worked well under sail, too. (No outboard in those days). They were built square across the stern with a notch cut for the sculling oar and four to six oarlocks.

So when we were off some, I told the woman to wrap up in an old sail lying in the bottom. She had on a heavy coat, claimed she wasn't cold. I insisted it would soon be damn cold outside; so she got down in the bottom of the boat and wrapped up.

In about an hour ebb as I figgered by land-sight, we were doing five knots. Not bad, I congratulated myself too soon.

The lady was a good talker; All I had to do was keep the boat out and listen to her. I was getting a big kick out of the way she 'foxed' her husband. She was never going back; all that was over; she had burnt her bridges. (Before too long I thought we both had;)

The time was slipping by and I was sculling easily, and then I noticed some ripples in the water on my starboard—'Shoal water' I thought and kept out some more.

It wasn't long before I heard swift running water ahead. In a few minutes we passed a sand bar on our port side and were going at a greater rate—possibly seven or eight knots. The swift ebb was lifting two feet high and seemed a hundred long and was a dirty brown color. My guts were drawn in a knot and I was scared stiff. The next hour was hell. I passed bars that were ten feet out of water and others just breaking through.

Sometimes we were going apace, others slowed down to a crawl. But the woman never stopped talking! I don't remember a thing after we passed the first bar—only hearing a voice talking,—talking!

It was now about four and I was wishing for daylight. The Bay was widening out so I knew we were pretty well down. We skimmed a few more bars pretty close and the water seemed to roll out in longer waves. Day began to break and we were slowing down.

Then glory be! the schooner loomed up not too far away. I was sculling as hard as I could; I wanted to get alongside before the up coming tide, and did I want something stronger than coffee.

The Skipper's ladder was over the side the crew standing by. Imagine my surprise when I had to wake the woman up.

All that time I thought she was talking—it was me:

Praying aloud!

TITLES BY PETHERIC PRESS

The Saladin Trial — 1844 - a Reprint
The McKay Motor Car — W. H. McCurdy
The Bottle Collector — Azor Vienneau
Nova Scotia Furniture — G. E. G. MacLaren
Antique Potteries of Nova Scotia — G. E. G. MacLaren
The Story of The Nova Scotia Tartan — Marjorie Major
A Pocketful of Nova Scotia History — No. 1 — Joseph Howe
Silversmiths and Related Craftsmen of the Atlantic Provinces — Donald C. Mackay
Vanishing Halifax — L. B. Jenson
Nova Scotia Sketchbook — L. B. Jenson
Wood and Stone — L. B. Jenson
Country Roads — L. B. Jenson
The River that Missed the Boat — Barbara Grantmyre
Daveys Pilots and the Sea Wolves — Catherine L. Brown

Also Publisher of

THE NOVA SCOTIA HISTORICAL QUARTERLY

PRINTED & BOUND
BY MCCURDY PRINTING CO. LTD.
HALIFAX, NOVA SCOTIA, CANADA

"These are tales of the sea from Nova Scotia's great age of sail. These chilling experiences and mysterious happenings in the famous Bay of Fundy come from the journal of one who sailed there around the turn of the century and was impressed enough by the accounts to record them."